MR. BELLOC OBJECTS
TO "THE OUTLINE OF HISTORY"

Hilaire Belloc

MR. BELLOC OBJECTS

TO "THE OUTLINE OF HISTORY"

BY

H. G. WELLS

With Portraits

NEW YORK

GEORGE H. DORAN COMPANY

COPYRIGHT, 1926,
BY GEORGE H. DORAN COMPANY

FOREWORD

IN the autumn of 1925 and the spring and summer of 1926 there was published a revised and illustrated version of the *Outline of History,* by Mr. H. G. Wells. There followed a series of articles by Mr. Belloc attacking this *Outline* and Mr. Wells. These articles were published in the Catholic *Universe,* in the *Southern Cross* of Cape Colony, in the American *Catholic Bulletin,* and possibly elsewhere. Every fortnight, keeping pace with the issue of the *Outline,* these attacks appeared; in all, twenty-four voluminous articles. They were grossly personal and provocative in tone, and no doubt a great joy and comfort to the faithful. Mr. Wells prepared a series of articles in reply; and as no one outside the public of these Catholic journals seemed to have heard of Mr. Belloc's attacks, he offered them to the editors concerned, proposing, if necessary, to give the use of this interesting matter to them without payment. Six articles he asked to have published— in reply to twenty-four. This offering was declined very earnestly by these editors. To the editor of the Catholic *Universe* Mr. Wells protested in the terms of the following letter:—

My Dear Sir,

I am sorry to receive your letter of May 19th. May I point out to you that Mr. Belloc has been attacking my reputation as a thinker, a writer, an impartial historian, and an educated person for four-and-twenty fortnights in the *Universe?* He has misquoted; he has misstated. Will your Catholic public tolerate no reply?

Under the stimulus of this remonstrance, the editor of the *Universe,* after a month's delay and various consultations with Mr. Belloc and the directors of his paper, offered Mr. Wells the "opportunity of correcting definite points of fact upon which he might have been misrepresented," but declined to allow him to defend his views or examine Mr. Belloc's logic and imputations in his columns. Mr. Wells was disinclined for a series of wrangles upon what might or might not be a "point of fact." He then offered his articles to various non-Catholic papers, but, with one accord, they expressed their lack of interest in either Mr. Belloc himself or in his exposition of Catholic ideas about natural selection, the origin of man, and the general course of history. Yet it seems to Mr. Wells that, regarded as a mental sample, Mr. Belloc is not without significance, and that the examination of the contemporary Catholic attitude towards the fundamental facts of history is a matter of interest beyond Catholic circles. Accordingly he has decided to issue these articles in the form of a book, and he has urged the publishers to advertise them, as freely as may be permitted, in the Catholic press. He has retained the "cross-heads" customary in journalistic writing.

CONTENTS

MR. BELLOC OBJECTS
TO "THE OUTLINE OF HISTORY"

I

MR. BELLOC'S ARTS OF CONTROVERSY

I AM the least controversial of men. Public
disputations have rarely attracted me. For
years I have failed to respond to Mr. Henry
Arthur Jones, who long ago invented a set of
opinions for me and invited me to defend them
with an enviable persistence and vigour. Occasionally I may have corrected some too gross
public misstatement about me—too often I fear
with the acerbity of the inexperienced. But now,
in my sixtieth year, I find myself drawn rather
powerfully into a disputation with Mr. Hilaire
Belloc. I bring an unskilled pen to the task.

I am responsible for an *Outline of History*
which has had a certain vogue. I will assume
that it is known by name to the reader. It is a
careful summary of man's knowledge of past
time. It has recently been reissued with considerable additions in an illustrated form, and Mr.
Belloc has made a great attack upon it. He declares that I am violently antagonistic to the
Catholic Church, an accusation I deny very earnestly, and he has produced a "Companion" to
this *Outline* of mine, following up the periodical
issue, part by part, in the *Universe* of London,

in the *Catholic Bulletin* of St. Paul, Minnesota, in the *Southern Cross* of Cape Colony, and possibly elsewhere, in which my alleged errors are exposed and confuted.

In the enthusiasm of advertisement before the "Companion" began to appear, these newspapers announced a work that would put Mr. Belloc among the great classical Catholic apologists, but I should imagine that this was before the completed manuscript of Mr. Belloc's work had come to hand, and I will not hold Catholics at large responsible for all Mr. Belloc says and does.

It is with this *Companion to the Outline of History* that I am to deal here. It raises a great number of very interesting questions, and there is no need to discuss the validity of the charge of Heresy that is levelled against me personally. I will merely note that I am conscious of no animus against Catholicism, and that in my *Outline* I accept the gospels as historical documents of primary value, defend Christianity against various aspersions of Gibbon's, and insist very strongly upon the rôle of the Church in preserving learning in Europe, consolidating Christendom, and extending knowledge from a small privileged class to the whole community. I do not profess to be a Christian. I am as little disposed to take sides between a Roman Catholic and a Protestant. Mr. Belloc will protest against that "Roman," but he must forgive it; I know no other way of distinguishing between his Church and Catholics not in communion with it, as I am between a pterodactyl and a bird.

DISCONCERTING POSE OF MR. BELLOC

In this art of controversy it is evident that great importance attaches to pose. This is plain from the very outset of Mr. Belloc's apologia. From the beginning I have to be put in my place, and my relationship to Mr. Belloc has to be defined. Accustomed as I am to see Mr. Belloc dodging about in my London club, and in Soho and thereabouts, and even occasionally appearing at a dinner-party, compactly stout, rather breathless and always insistently garrulous, I am more than a little amazed at his opening. He has suddenly become aloof from me. A great gulf of manner yawns between us. "Hullo, Belloc!" is frozen on my lips, dies unuttered. He advances upon me in his Introduction with a gravity of utterance, a dignity of gesture, rare in sober, God-fearing men. There is a slow, formal compliment or so. I have, I learn, "a deservedly popular talent in fiction." I am sincere, an honest soul. My intentions are worthy. But the note changes; he declares I am a "Protestant writing for Protestants," and there is danger that my *Outline* may fall into Catholic hands. Some Catholics may even be infected with doubt. His style thickens with emotion at this thought, and he declares: "One Catholic disturbed in his faith is more important than twenty thousand or a hundred thousand or a million of the average reading public of England and America.'' That is why he is giving me his attention, syndicating these articles and swelling himself up so strongly against me. That is why he now proposes to exhibit and explain and expose me in the sight of all mankind. It is controversy, and everyday manners are in abeyance.

The controversial pose reveals itself further. The compliments and civilities thin out and vanish. Mr. Belloc becomes more magisterial, relatively larger, relatively graver, with every paragraph. He assumes more definitely the quality of a great scholar of European culture and European reputation, a trained, distinguished, universally accepted historian. With what is evidently the dexterity of an expert controversialist and with an impressiveness all his own, he seems to look over and under and round the man he knows, and sketches in the man he proposes to deal with, his limitations, his pitiful limitations, the characteristics, the disagreeable characteristics, that disfigure him. It is a new Wells, a most extraordinary person. I learn with amazement the particulars with which it is necessary to instruct that Catholic soul in danger before the matter of my book can be considered. I see myself in the lurid illumination of Catholic truth.

Remarkable Portrait of Mr. Wells

To begin with, I am "an intense patriot." This will surprise many readers. I dread its effect on Mr. Henry Arthur Jones, whose favourite tune upon the megaphone for years has been that I am the friend of every country but my own. Will he intervene with a series of articles to "My dear Belloc"? I hope not. I might plead that almost any chapter of the *Outline of History* could be quoted against this proposition. But Mr. Belloc is ruthless; he offers no evidence for his statement, no foothold for a counter-plea. He just says it, very clearly, very emphatically several times over, and he says it, as I realise very soon, because it is the necessary preliminary to his next still more damaging exposures.

They are that I am an Englishman "of the Home Counties and London Suburbs"—Mr. Belloc, it seems, was born all over Europe—that my culture is entirely English, that I know nothing of any language or literature or history or science but that of England. And from this his creative invention sweeps on to a description of this new Wells he is evoking to meet his controversial needs. My admiration grows. I resist an impulse to go over at once to Mr. Belloc's side. This, for example, is splendid. This new Wells, this suburban English Protestant, has written his *Outline of History* because, says Mr. Belloc, "he does not know that 'foreigners' (as he would call them) have general histories.''

That ''as he would call them'' is the controversial Mr. Belloc rising to his best.

Mr. Belloc, I may note in passing, does not cite any of these general histories to which he refers. It would surely make an interesting list and help the Catholic soul in danger to better reading. The American reader, at whose prejudices this stuff about my patriotism is presumably aimed, would surely welcome a competing Outline by a ''foreigner.'' Mr. Belloc might do worse things than a little translation work.

Then the Royal College of Science shrivels at his touch to a mechanics' institute, and the new Wells, I learn, ''does really believe from the bottom of his heart all that he read in the text-books of his youth.'' The picture of this new Wells, credulous, uncritical devourer of the text-books supplied by his suburban institute, inveterate Protestant, grows under the pen of this expert controversialist. I have next to be presented as a low-class fellow with a peculiar bias against the ''Gentry of my own country,'' and this is accordingly done. ''Gentlemen'' with whom I have quarrelled are hinted at darkly—a pretty touch of fantasy. A profound and incurable illiteracy follows as a matter of course.

Gathering Courage of Mr. Belloc

Mr. Belloc's courage gathers with the elaboration of his sketch. He is the type to acquiesce readily in his own statements, and one can see him persuading himself as he goes along that this really is the Wells he is up against. If so, what is there to be afraid of? If there is a twinge of doubt, he can always go back and read what he has written. The phraseology loses its earlier discretion, gets more pluckily abusive. Presently words like "ignorance" and "blunders" and "limited instruction" come spluttering from those ready nibs. Follows "childish" and "pitiable" and "antiquated nonsense." Nothing to substantiate any of it—just saying it. So Mr. Belloc goes his way along the primrose path of controversy. He takes a fresh sip or so from his all too complaisant imagination. New inspirations come. I have "copied" things from the "wrong" books. That "copied" is good! One can see that base malignant Wells fellow, in his stuffy room all hung with Union Jacks, with the "wrong," the *"Protestant"* book flattened out before him, copying, copying; his tongue following his laborious pen. Presently I read: "It is perhaps asking too much of our author to adopt a strictly scientific attitude." This, from an adept in that mixture of stale politics and gossip which passed for history in the days of Mr. Belloc's reading, to even the least of Huxley's students, is stupendous!

Still he swells and swells with self-importance and self-induced contempt for his silent and invisible antagonist. The pen runs on, for does not the Catholic press wait for its latest great apologist? The thin film of oily politeness in the opening paragraphs is long since gone and done with, and Mr. Hilaire Belloc is fully himself again and remains himself, except for one or two returns to patronising praise and the oil squirt, for the rest of these remarkable papers.

His are, I suppose, the accepted manners of controversy—and what wonderful manners they are! I note them, but I cannot emulate them.

There is, however, one reference to the unlettered suburbanism of this ideal Wells too good to lose. I had almost let it slip by. It is an allusion to a certain publication in French. "There may be no translation," Mr. Belloc throws out superbly at the height of his form, "but Mr. Wells ought to have heard of"—the out-of-date monograph in question. "There may be no translation . . ."! How feeble sounds my protest that for all practical purposes I read French as well as I do English, and that in all probability if it came to using a German, Spanish, Portuguese, or Italian scientific work I could give Mr. Belloc points and a beating.

REFLECTIONS UPON THE REAL MR. BELLOC

But I have said enough to justify incidentally my habitual avoidance of the arts of controversy. I cannot inflate myself in this fashion. I cannot do the counter to this attitude. I was born and I shall die "familiar." What seems to make Mr. Belloc feel brave and happy would make me feel sick. On this he has presumed overmuch. There are limits to my notorious gentleness and modesty, and they have been reached by Mr. Belloc in these articles. His skill is undeniable; no other writer could better his unpremeditated condescension, his apparently inadvertent insults. And yet the facts beneath all this insolent posturing are quite well known and easily verifiable. I cannot imagine whom it is intended to deceive for any length of time.

Mr. Belloc is a man four years my junior, and his academic career was briefer and not more brilliant than mine. Since he came down from Oxford to the world of London thirty years ago, he has done no original historical work of any distinction. He has been a popular writer as I have been a popular writer, and he is no more if no less a scholar than I am. There has been much incidental and inconsequent brightness in his discursive career—funny verses and stories, an amusing rather than a serious period in Parliament, much pamphleteering, lecturing and speaking; he has been active and erratic; now he would be urging on an anti-Semitic campaign; now, in association with Horatio Bottomley, attempting to hound Masterman, his old friend and rival, out of politics; the war made him the most confident of military "experts," and he has done quite a number of clever revivifications of this or that historical event. That is his record. It gives him a respectable position in the republic of letters, in which also my position is respectable. No doubt he has every right and very considerable qualifications for the criticism of such a popular work as my *Outline*. But there is nothing in his career and nothing in his quality to justify this pose of erudition and insolent superiority he assumes towards me, and which he has made an integral part of his attack. He has assumed it entirely in relation to this controversy. He has thrown ordinary courtesy and good manners to the winds because only in that way can he hope for a controversial advantage over me.

The Clue to Mr. Belloc's Disconcerting Pose

This disconcerting pose is part of his attack. That is why I am obliged to discuss it here. Upon many points the attack is almost pure pose; there is no tangible argument at all. It is very important to note that and bear that in mind. It has to be borne in mind when Mr. Belloc is accused of inordinate vanity or of not knowing his place in the world. I doubt even if he is really very vain. I realised long ago that his apparent arrogance is largely the self-protection of a fundamentally fearful man. He is a stout fellow in a funk. He is the sort of man who talks loud and fast for fear of hearing the other side. There is a frightened thing at the heart of all this burly insolence. He has a faith to defend, and he is not sure of his defence. That mitigates much of his offence, even if it mitigates little of his offensiveness.

Let me say a word or so more of excuse and explanation for him. These personalities of his are, so to speak, not a personal matter. There is more in them than that. Mr. Belloc's attack upon my *Outline* does not stand alone among his activities; it is part of a larger controversy he wages against the modern, the non-Catholic vision of the world. He has carried on that controversy since his Balliol days. The exigencies that oblige him to pretend, against his better knowledge and common civility, that I am petty and provincial and patriotic and wilfully ignorant and pitifully out-of-date, oblige him to pretend as much about most of those who stand for modern science and a modern interpretation of history. He would pretend as hard about Sir Ray Lankester, for example, or about Professor Gilbert Murray or Sir Harry Johnston or Professor Barker, as he does about me. It is a general system of pretence. It is a necessary part of—I will not say of *the* Catholic attitude, but of *his* Catholic attitude towards modern knowledge.

The necessity for a pose involving this pretence is not very difficult to understand. Long before Mr. Belloc embarked upon the present dispute he had become the slave of a tactical fiction, which reiteration had made a reality for him. He evoked the fiction as early, I believe, as his Oxford days. It may have been very effective at Oxford— among the undergraduates. Then perhaps it was consciously a defensive bluff, but certainly it is no longer that. He has come at last to believe absolutely in this creature of his imagination. He has come to believe this: that there is a vast "modern European" culture of which the English-speaking world knows nothing, of which the non-Catholic world knows nothing, and with which he is familiar. It is on his side. It is always on his side. It is simply and purely Belloccian. He certainly believes it is there. It sustains his faith. It assuages the gnawing attacks of self-criticism that must come to him in the night. Throughout these papers he is constantly referring to this imaginary stuff—without ever coming to precisions. Again and again and again and again— and again and again and again, he alludes to this marvellous "European" science and literature, beyond our ken.

He does not quote it; it does not exist for him to quote; but he believes that it exists. He waves his hand impressively in the direction in which it is supposed to be. It is his stand-by, his refuge, his abiding fortress. But, in order to believe in it, it is necessary for him to believe that no other English-speaking men can even read French, and that their scepticism about it is based on some "provincial" prejudice or some hatred of Catholics, or southern people, or "Dagoes," or "foreigners," or what you will. That is why *Nature* wilfully ignores the wonderful science of this "Europe"; and why our Royal Society has no correspondence with it. But he has to imagine it is there and make his readers imagine it is there, and that there is this conspiracy of prejudice to ignore it, before he can even begin to put up any appearance of a case against such a résumé of current knowledge as the *Outline of History*.

GRACEFUL CONCESSIONS TO MR. BELLOC

All this rough and apparently irrelevant stuff about his own great breadth and learning and my profound ignorance and provincialism, to which he has devoted his two introductory papers, is therefore the necessary prelude to putting over this delusion. That stream of depreciation is not the wanton personal onslaught one might suppose it to be at the first blush. If he has appeared to glorify himself and belittle me, it is for greater controversial ends than a mere personal score. We are dealing with a controversialist here and a great apologist, and for all I know these may be quite legitimate methods in this, to me, unfamiliar field.

Few people will be found to deny Mr. Belloc a considerable amplitude of mind in his undertaking, so soon as they get thus far in understanding him. Before he could even set about syndicating this *Companion to the Outline of History* he had to incite a partisan receptivity in the Catholic readers to whom he appeals, by declaring that a violent hatred for their Church is the guiding motive of my life. He had to ignore a considerable array of facts to do that, and he has ignored them with great courage and steadfastness. He had to arouse an indifferent Catholic public to a sense of urgent danger by imposing this figure of a base, inveterate, and yet finally contemptible enemy upon it. His is a greater task than mere dragon-slaying. He had to create the dragon before he could become the champion. And then, with his syndication arrangements complete, while abusing me industriously for ignorance, backwardness, and general intellectual backwoodism, he had to write the whole of these articles without once really opening that Humbert safe of knowledge which is his sole capital in this controversy. Time after time he refers to it. Never once does he quote it. At most he may give us illusive peeps. . . .

Now and then as we proceed I shall note these illusive peeps.

I can admire great effort even when it is ill-

directed, and to show how little I bear him a
grudge for the unpleasant things he has induced
himself to write about me, and for the still more
unpleasant things he tempts me—though I resist
with a success that gratifies me—to write about
him, I contemplate a graceful compliment to Mr.
Belloc. In spite of the incurable ignorance of
French and that "dirty Dago" attitude towards
foreigners Mr. Belloc has so agreeably put upon
me, it is my habit to spend a large part of the
winter in a house I lease among the olive terraces
of Provence. There is a placard in one corner of
my study which could be rather amusingly covered
with the backs of dummy books. I propose to
devote that to a collection of Mr. Belloc's authorities. There shall be one whole row at least of
the Bulletins of the Madame Humbert Society,
and all the later researches of the Belloc Acad-
emy of Anonymous Europeans, bound in bluff
leather. There will be *Finis Darwinis* by Hilario
Belloccio, and *Hist. Eccles.* by Hilarius Belloccius.
I may have occasion to refer to other leading
authorities in the course of this controversy. I
shall add to it as we proceed.

And so, having examined, explained, disposed
of, and in part apologised for, Mr. Belloc's personalities and the pervading inelegance of his
manners, I shall turn with some relief from this
unavoidably personal retort to questions of a more
general interest. I propose as my first study of
these modern Catholic apologetics, so valiantly

produced by Mr. Belloc and so magnificently published and displayed by the Catholic press, to follow our hero's courageous but unsteady progress
through the mysteries of Natural Selection. And
after that we shall come to Original Sin and Human Origins in the light of Mr. Belloc's science
and the phantom science of those phantom naturalists and anthropologists he calls to his assist-
ance.

II

THE THEORY OF NATURAL SELECTION STATED

M Y first article upon Mr. Belloc's *Companion to the Outline of History* dealt, much against my inclination and as charitably and amiably as possible, with the oddities of Mr. Belloc's manner and method, and those remarkable non-existent "European authorities" to whom he appeals habitually in moments of argumentative stress. I do not propose to go on thus girding at Mr. Belloc. He is a Catholic apologist, endorsed by Catholic authorities, and there is matter of very great importance for our consideration in what he has to say about the history of life and mankind.

After his second paper is finished his abuse of me becomes merely incidental or indirect. He goes on to a staggering rush at Natural Selection. Let us see to where Catholic thought has got—if Mr. Belloc is to be trusted—in relation to this very fundamental matter.

It is Mr. Belloc's brilliant careless way to begin most of his arguments somewhere about the middle and put the end first. His opening peroration, so to speak, is a proclamation that this "Natural Selection"—whatever it is—is "an old and done-

for theory of Darwin and Wallace." It is "a
laughing-stock for half a generation among compe-
tent men." Mr. George Bernard Shaw does not
believe in it! G. B. S. among the Fathers! That
wonderful non-existent "latest European work"
which plays so large a part in Mr. Belloc's dialec-
tic is summoned briefly, its adverse testimony is
noted, and it is dismissed to the safe again. And
then there is a brief statement of how these two
vile fellows, Darwin and Wallace, set out upon
this reprehensible theorising. What a ruthless
exposé it is of the true motives of scientific people!

"The process of thought was as follows:
" 'There is no Mind at work in the universe; therefore changes of this sort must
come from blind chance or at least *mechan-
ically*. At all costs we must get rid of the
idea of design: of a desired end conceived
in a Creative Mind. Here is a theory which
will make the whole process entirely mechan-
ical and dead, and get rid of the necessity
for a Creator.' "

And so having invented and then as it were
visited and spat upon the derided and neglected
tomb of Natural Selection and assured us that
God, Mr. Shaw, "European opinion," and all good
Catholics are upon his side, Mr. Belloc plucks up
courage and really begins to write about Natural
Selection.

NATURAL SELECTION IS PURE COMMON-SENSE

What is this Natural Selection which has been dead for half a century, but which Mr. Belloc still exerts himself industriously through four long papers to kill all over again? It is the purest common-sense, the most obvious deduction from obvious facts. I have set out the idea as plainly as I could in the *Outline of History* Mr. Belloc is attacking. It is put so plainly there that, before he can begin to argue against it, he has to misstate it; he has to tell the story all over again in his own words and get it suitably askew. It was quite open to him to quote from my account, but he preferred to compile his own misstatement. Indeed, in all this argument against Natural Selection he never once quotes my actual words. He paraphrases throughout. He has put some words between inverted commas in one place, so as inadvertently to produce the impression that they are mine, but they are not mine.

Now the facts upon which the idea of Natural Selection rests are matters of universal knowledge. "Every species of living thing is continually dying and being born again as a multitude of fresh individuals"; that is the primary fact. No species seems to be perfectly adapted to its conditions, and even the happiest species tends to multiply until it is in a state of need and pressure. So far surely we are dealing with things beyond dispute. And next comes the fact of individual-

ity. Every living unit is individual with a difference of its own. Every individual has its own distinctive differences, and each of these differences
may or may not be an advantage or a disadvantage. Individuals with advantageous differences
will generally get on better in life, prosper and so
be able to breed more freely, than those with dis-
advantageous differences. Offspring have a tendency to repeat the distinctive differences of their
parents. Therefore, taking a species as a whole
by the million or billion or million billion—for
few species of animals or plants are represented
by fewer individuals than a million—there will
be in each successive generation a greater number
of individuals with the differences that are advantageous relative to the number with disad-
vantages. In other words, the average of the
species will have moved more or less in the direction of the advantageous differences, whatever
they may be, and however numerous they may be.
If, for example, the species is chased and has to
climb or run for it, there will be rather more good
climbers and sprinters in the new generation.
There may be other dangers and other needs;
they will not affect the premium set on quickness
and the fate of the slow. And if the circumstances
of the species continue to press in the same direction, the movement of the average will be in the
same direction in this respect for so long as they
continue to press. Over a few score or even a few
hundred generations, and under conditions not

very strenuous, a species may not change very much. It may seem to be *fixed* in its general characteristics, just as the continents seem to be fixed in their general outline. But, as the range of time extends and the pressure of necessity continues, the change becomes more striking.

Natural Selection Has Nothing to Do with the Origin of Variations

That is the process of Natural Selection, the "laughing-stock" of Mr. Belloc's mysterious conclave of "European" savants. Natural Selection has nothing to do with the reason for the differences between individuals. It has no more to do with those than gravitation has to do with the differences in the heaviness of different substances. But it is necessary to state as much here, because in some queer muddled way Mr. Belloc seems to be persuaded that it has. These differences may arise by pure chance; they may come about through the operation of complex laws, they may come in shoals and have their seasons. These things have nothing to do with Natural Selection.

Now, Wallace and Darwin were two excellent Europeans who happened to be interested in natural history. In spite of the sinister motives invented for them by Mr. Belloc, I doubt if any Catholic sufficiently educated to have read their lives will agree that they had even a latent animus against Catholic truth or even a subconscious desire to "get rid of a Creator" in their minds. They no more thought of "getting rid of a Creator" when humbly and industriously they gathered their facts and put fact to fact than an honest bricklayer thinks of "getting rid of a Creator" when he lays his bricks with care and builds a sound piece of wall. They went about the world studying natural history. They considered life with a patience and thoroughness and freedom from preconceptions beyond the imagination of a man of Mr. Belloc's habits. They found no such "fixity of species" as he is inspired to proclaim. They found much evidence of a progressive change in species, and they saw no reason to explain it by a resort to miracles or magic. A Catholic priest of the Anglican communion named Malthus had written a very interesting and suggestive book upon over-population and the consequent struggle for existence between individuals. It turned the attention of both these diligent and gifted observers to just that process of Natural Selection I have stated. Independently both of them came to the conclusions that species changed age by age and without any necessary limits, and mainly through the sieve of Natural Selection, and that, given a sufficient separation to reduce or prevent interbreeding and a sufficient difference in the selective conditions at work, two parts of the same species might change in different directions, so as at last to become distinct and separate species.

Darwin's book upon the subject was called *The Origin of Species*. It was a very modest and sufficient title. He did not even go to the length of calling it the origin of genera or orders or classes. He did not at first apply it to man.

This is the theory of the origin of species through Natural Selection. It was not pretended by either of these pioneers that Natural Selection was the sole way through which the differences of species came about. For example, Darwin devoted a considerable part of his working life to such collateral modes of differentiation as the hypothesis that Sexual Selection also had its share. Criticism has whittled down that share to practically negligible proportions, but I note the hypothesis here because it absolutely disposes of the assertion which Mr. Belloc hammers on the table, that the Theory of Natural Selection excludes any other mode of specific differentiation.

Testing the Theory

Very rapidly this conception of Natural Selection was extended by naturalists until it came to be regarded as the general process of life. They came to realise that all species, all genera, all classes of life, whatever else may be happening to them, are and always have been varying through the process of Natural Selection, some rapidly, some slowly; some so slowly as hardly to change at all through vast ages. I have stated the *a priori* case by which, given birth and death and individuality and changing conditions and sufficient time, it appears logically inevitable that the change and differentiation of species *must* occur, and must be now going on. If we had no material evidence at all it would still be possible to infer the evolution of species.

That *a priori* case has never been answered, and it seems to me unanswerable. But scientific men, with their obstinate preference for observation and experiment over mere logical gymnastics, rarely rest their convictions on a *priori* cases. A sustaining scepticism is a matter of conscience with them. To them an *a priori* case is merely a theory—that is to say, a generalisation under trial. For nearly three-quarters of a century, therefore, biologists have been examining whatever instances they could discover that seemed to contradict this assumption that the process of specific change under Natural Selection is the general condition of life. To this day this view is still called the Theory of Natural Selection, though to a great number it has come to have the substantial quality of an embracing fact.

It would have been amusing if Mr. Belloc had told us more of his ideas of the scientific world. Apparently he knows scarcely anything of museums or laboratories or the spirit and methods of research. And manifestly he has not the faintest suspicion of the way in which the whole world of vital phenomena has been ransacked and scrutinised to test, correct, supplement, amplify, or alter this great generalisation about life. He probably shares the delusion of most other men in the street, that scientific theories are scientific finalities, that they are supposed to be as ultimate as the dogmas of some infallible religion. He imagines them put over chiefly by asseveration, just as the assertions of a polemical journalist are put over. He has still to learn that theories are trial material, testing targets, directives for research. Shooting at established theories is the normal occupation of the scientific investigator. Mr. Belloc's figure of the scientific investigator is probably a queer, frowsty, and often, alas! atheistical individual, poking about almost aimlessly among facts in the hope of hitting upon some "discovery" or "getting rid of a God." He does not understand the tense relevance of the vast amount of work in progress. But for three-quarters of a century the thought and work of myriads of people round and about the world have borne directly or almost directly upon the probing, sounding, testing, of the theory of Natural Selection. It stands clarified and, it would seem, impregnable to-day.

Some Irrelevant Questions

Among questions bearing upon it but not directly attacking it has been the discussion of the individual difference. For example, are differ-

ences due to individual experiences ever inherited?
Or are only inherent differences transmissible?
What rôle is played by what one might call "normal," relatively slight differences, and what by
the "sports" and abnormal births in specific
change? Do species under stress, and feeding on
strange food or living in unaccustomed climates,
betray any exceptional tendency to produce ab-
normality? Have there been, so to speak, storms
and riots of variation in some cases? Can differences establish themselves while outer necessity
remains neutral? Can variations amounting to
specific differences in colour and form arise as a
sort of play of the germ plasm and be tolerated
rather than selected by nature? In what manner
do normal differences arise? What happens to
differences in cases of hybridisation? Here are
sample questions that have been the seeds of
splendid work and great arguments. Some of
them were already under discussion in Darwin's
time; he was a pioneer in such explorations; many
ideas of his have stood the test of time, and
many suggestions he threw out have been dis-
proved. When some casual "may be" of Darwin's is examined and set aside, it is the custom
of polemical journalists to rush about and proclaim to all who may be sufficiently ill-informed
to listen that Darwin is "exploded." Such ex-
plosions of Darwin are constantly recurring like
gun-fire near a garrison town, and still he remains. None of these subsidiary questions affect

the stability of this main generalisation of biology, the Theory of Natural Selection.

The actual attack and testing of the Theory of Natural Selection have yielded negative results. The statement of the theory may have been made finer and exacter, that is all. And yet the conditions of its survival have been very exacting. If the theory is to stand, the whole of plant and animal life in time and space must be arranged in a certain order. It must be possible to replace classification by a genealogical tree. Every form must fall without difficulty into its proper place in that tree. If it is true that birds are descended from reptiles or men from apes, then there must be no birds before the reptiles appear, and no men before apes. The geological record is manifestly a mere fragmentary history, still for the most part unread, but, however fragmentary it is, it must be consistent. One human skull in the coal measures blows the whole theory to atoms. The passage from form to form must be explicable by intermediate types capable of maintaining themselves; there may be gaps in the record, but there must be no miraculous leaps in the story. If an animal living in the air is to be considered as a lineal descendant of some animal living in the water, then the structure of the former bit by bit and step by step must be shown to be adapted, modified, changed about from that of the latter; it must have ears for water-hearing modified for air-hearing, and its heart and breathing arrange-

ments must be shown to be similarly changed
over, and so on for all its structure. All these
requirements will follow naturally from the necessities of a process of Natural Selection. They follow logically upon no other hypothesis. They are
not demanded, for example, by the idea of a
Creator continually interfering with and rectify-
ing some stately, unaccountable process of "Evolution," which seems to be Mr. Belloc's idea—so
far as he ventures to display any idea of his own
—in the matter. Such things as vestigial structures and a number of odd clumsinesses in living
things—many still very imperfect adaptations to
an erect position, for example—become grotesque
in relation to such a view. A Creator who put
needless or inconvenient fish structures into the
anatomy of a land animal and made the whole
fauna and flora of the land a patch-up of aquatic
forms of life must be not so much a Divinity as a
Pedant. But it is the burthen of the whole beautiful science of comparative anatomy that the structure of animals and plants, and their succession in
time, fall exactly into the conditions defined by the
Theory of Natural Selection. In the most lovely
and intricate detail, in a vast multitude of ex-
amples, in plants and in animals alike, this theme
of the adaptation of pre-existing structure is
worked out.

We should in accordance with the Theory of
Natural Selection expect to find traces of the
ancestral form, not only in the lay-out of the adult

animal, but in every phase of its life history, and that, in fact, is just what we do find. There is no more fascinating branch of comparative anatomy than embryology. Each life cycle we discuss tends to repeat the ancestral story, and only under the stress of necessity does it undergo modification at any point. There is little toleration in the life process for unnecessary divergencies. Economies are effected by short cuts and reductions, and special fœtal structures are granted reluctantly. So that even in man we find peeping through the adaptations imposed upon the human type by its viviparous necessities, and in spite of the advantage of every economy of force, memories, for example, of the gill slits, of the fish heart and kidney, of the reptilian skull, of the mammalian tail. I mention this fact in the *Outline,* and upon it Mr. Belloc comments in a manner that leaves one's doubts poised between his honesty and his intelligence. He declares, which is totally untrue, that I "repeat the old Victorian tag"—I doubt if there ever was such a tag—that the embryo "climbs up the family tree." He puts these words in inverted commas as though I have really adopted and used them, and for the life of me it is only by straining my charity to the utmost that I can accept that this was an accident. Of course every text-book of embryology for the last forty years has made it perfectly plain, as I have stated here, that the life cycle can be and is modified at any point, and that an embryo has much more serious work in hand than reciting its family history. It betrays its ancestral origins to analysis; but that is an altogether different matter. Mr. Belloc, however, is so densely ignorant himself upon these questions that he can imagine, or think it worth while to pretend to imagine and attempt to persuade his readers by the expedient of these inverted commas, that I entertain such a view. And then follow this, which I quote that the reader may the better understand a certain occasional acerbity in my allusions to Mr. Belloc:—

"He doesn't know that Vailleton of Montpellier has knocked the last nail into the coffin of that facile and superficial Victorian shortcut (and blind alley). He has probably never heard of Vailleton, and when he does he will suspect him for a foreigner. That is what I mean by being provincial and not abreast of one's time."

It is perfectly true that I have never heard of any Vailleton in biological science. Nor has anyone else. There is "no sich person." Perhaps Mr. Belloc has not been able to read the manuscript of some adviser, or his memory may have played a trick upon him. Possibly he has in mind that eminent Victorian embryologist, Vialleton, who, so far from being the very newest thing in "European" biology, must now be getting on for seventy. He is half-way back to Haeckel, the originator of the family-tree idea, a German embryologist and not, as a matter of fact, the Victorian English Protestant Mr. Belloc supposes him to be. Possibly years and years ago some French student may have run away with the idea that embryos conscientiously repeat their phylogeny, and Professor Vialleton may have thought it well to discuss this idea in one of his books. It is not an idea I have ever entertained, much less stated, and its only interest here is that it gives Mr. Belloc a chance of showing how rudely he can set out his inaccuracies and his misconceptions.

But this is an incidental comment. I will reserve for my next section a consideration of the remarkable arguments—"crushing arguments" the enthusiastic cross-heads of his editor declare them to be—that Mr. Belloc produces against this view of life as being in a state of change under the action of Natural Selection, that I have put here before the reader.

III

MR. BELLOC AS A SPECIMEN CRITIC OF NATURAL SELECTION

THE chief arguments against the Theory of Natural Selection with which Mr. Belloc has favoured us are neatly set out by him in two triads. His passion for orderly arrangement is greater than his logic, and we shall find that the second and third arguments of his second triad are substantially the same. He is rather exceptionally ignorant of modern scientific literature, and his arguments do not cover all the countervailing considerations upon which systematic observation and research work have been based—the speculations of Dr. Fairfield Osborn would have been a godsend for him—but the things he has to say are conveniently simple; they embody some prevalent misconceptions, and they will be useful in accentuating the more salient points in my account of the theory given in my second paper.

He produces first certain remarkable *a priori* arguments—his "three *a prior* arguments." The first is beautifully absurd. It is difficult to believe it is advanced in anything but a spirit of burlesque. He says that an advantage is not an advantage. He says that an advantage does not give an advantage unless it is combined with other advantages. You will think I am misrepresenting him. Then please read this:—

"(1) The advantageous differences making for survival are not of one kind in any particular case, but of an indefinitely large number (*e.g.*, climate getting colder needs not only warmer coat, but power to digest new food, protective colouring so as not to show dark against snow, etc., an indefinitely large number of qualities). Now the chance of *all* being combined (and co-ordinated) in a single individual, *without design, accidentally,* let alone of their thus appearing in many individuals *accidentally and without design,* approximates to zero."

This is, so to speak, the short uncompleted form of the first argument. It is expanded later to a copiousness too great to admit of quotation. This expansion carries the statement right to its conclusion, that only an individual possessing all the possible differences that are advantageous at any particular time can survive. Otherwise its differences have no "survival value." They may be advantages, but not sufficient advantages to score an advantage. I know this sounds tipsy, but there it is in black and white in Mr. Belloc's wonderful Article V for any one to consult. It follows plainly that, except for a miracle, every species must be exterminated in every generation. I can see no other way out of it. No individual, he declares, can survive without the full set of advantageous differences, and the chance of any individual having the full set of advantageous differences, he declares after some abstruse verbal gestures, is zero. There is Mr. Belloc with his unfailing logic, his clear mathematical demonstration, and all the rest of it. There is the lucid Latin mind shining above my Nordic fog! Yet the previous generation got along without any of the set! And species do survive.

Did Mr. Belloc imagine he was saying something else? It is not for me to speculate. Helping out an antagonist in a controversy is apt to be resented. He has, I think, simply got into a muddle here, and he is not sufficiently self-critical to get out of it again. So he tries to muddle through. It is quite reasonable to say that when a species is under stress of changing conditions it is usual for the need for adaptation to be felt upon a number of points and not simply upon one, and that, since every advantage counts, the individuals with the greatest combination of advantageous differences have the best chances. But that does not alter the fact that even a single advantage is an advantage. What happens in nature is not an extermination of all who are not completely in the fashion of the new differences. That seems to be Mr. Belloc's idea, but it is a wrong idea. What does happen is a diminution in each generation of the number of the disadvantaged in relation to the number of the advantaged.

That is quite another affair. Mr. Belloc has not grasped this. His third *a priori* argument shows as much even more plainly than his first, and to that I shall presently come.

MR. BELLOC'S MENTAL INDIGESTION

I fancy this stuff he has written here is an outcome of an indigestion of Samuel Butler by Mr. Belloc. I should not have thought Mr. Belloc had read Samuel Butler, and I doubt if he has read him much. But there is a decided echo of *Luck or Cunning* in the one indistinct paragraph in which, without committing himself too deeply, Mr. Belloc seems to convey his own attitude towards the procedure of Evolution. "Design," whatever that is, is at work, and Natural Selection is not. "There is an innate power possessed by the living thing to attempt its own adaptation." It is quite a delusion apparently that rabbits that cannot run or sparrows that are not quick on the wing are killed off more frequently than the smarter fellows. That never happens, though to the atheistically minded it may seem to happen. If it happens, it would "get rid of a God." But there are rabbits which, unlike Mrs. Micawber, do make an effort. You must understand that all creation, inspired by design, is striving. The good fungus says to itself, "Redder and more spots will benefit me greatly," and tries and tries, and presently there are redder hues and more spots. Or a happily inspired fish says: "There is a lot of food on land and the life is more genteel there, so let me get lungs." And presently it gets lungs. Some day Mr. Belloc must take a holiday in Sussex and flap about a bit and get himself some wings and demonstrate all this. But perhaps this is caricature, and Mr. Belloc when he talks about that "innate disposition" just means nothing very much—just an attempt or something. I will not pretend to understand Mr. Belloc fully upon this point.

Mr. Belloc's Bird-Lizard

I will return to the essential misconception of the Theory of Natural Selection betrayed in this first *a priori* when I consider Mr. Belloc's third feat of logic. But first let me glance at his second. In this he says, very correctly, that every stage in the evolution of a living creature must be a type capable of maintaining itself and every change must be an advantageous change. I have noted this very obvious point already in my second paper. But then Mr. Belloc instructs us that the chances of its being so are, for no earthly reason, zero—that fatal zero again!—and goes on to a passage so supremely characteristic that it must be read to be believed:—

> "A bird has wings with which it can escape its enemies. If it began as a reptile without wings—when, presumably, it had armour or some other aid to survival—what of the in-

H. G. Wells.

LOW.

terval? Natural Selection sets out to change a reptile's leg into a bird's wing and the scales of its armour into feathers. It does so by making the leg less and less of a leg for countless ages, and by infinite minute gradations, gradually turning the scales into feathers.

"By the very nature of the theory *each stage* in all these millions is an advantage over the last towards survival! The thing has only to be stated for its absurdity to appear. Compare the 'get away' chances of a lizard at one end of the process or a sparrow at the other with some poor beast that had to try and scurry off on half-wings! or to fly with half-legs!

"Postulate a design, say, 'Here was something in the making,' and the process is explicable, especially if fairly rapid so as to bridge over the dangerously weak stage of imperfection. Postulate Natural Selection and it is manifestly impossible."

Let us note a few things of which Mr. Belloc shows himself to be unaware in this amusing display of perplexity. In the first place he does not know that the Mesozoic reptiles most closely resembling birds were creatures walking on their hind-legs, with a bony structure of the loins and a backbone already suggestive of the avian anatomy. Nor is he aware that in the lowliest of living birds the fore-limbs are mere flappers, that the feathers are simpler in structure than any other bird's feathers, and that the general development of a bird's feather points plainly to the elongation of a scale. He has never learnt that feathers came before wings, and that at first they had to do, not with flying, but with protection against cold. Yet all this was under his nose in the *Outline of History* in text and picture. The transition from a quilled to a feathered dinosaur presents indeed no imaginative difficulties, and the earliest birds ran and did not fly. One of the earliest known extinct birds is *Hesperornis,* a wingless diving bird. It is figured on page 30, and there is another bird on page 34 that Mr. Belloc might ponder with advantage. A whole great section of living birds, like the ostrich and the emu, have no trace in their structure of any ancestral flying phase; their breast-bones are incapable of carrying the necessary muscular attachments.

But after the feather was fully developed it opened up great possibilities of a strong and light extension of the flapper, helpful in running or useful in leaps from tree to tree. *Archæopteryx,* another early bird, which is also figured in the *Outline,* has a sort of bat-wing fore-limb with feathers instead of membrane. It was a woodland creature, and flew as a flying fox or a flying lemur or even a bat flies. All these facts are widely known, and all that trouble about the half-leg, half-wing, dissolves before them. But consider what a hash they make of Mr. Belloc's argument, and how pitifully it scurries off before them on its nondescript stumps of pretentious half-knowledge, half-impudence! So much for zero the second.

TROUBLES OF MR. BELLOC AS A MATRIMONIAL AGENT

The final of this wonderful trinity of *a prioris* is a repetition of an argument advanced ages ago by Queen Victoria's Lord Salisbury, when he was President of the British Association. Even then it struck people that he had been poorly coached for the occasion. Assuming that one or two individuals have got all these "survival value" differences in the correct proportions—against which the chances are zero—how by any theory of Natural Selection are we to suppose they will meet, breed, and perpetuate them? So this argument runs. The chances are again declared to be zero, the third zero, and Mr. Belloc, I gather, calls in Design again here and makes his Creative Spirit, which has already urged these two individuals, lions, or liver flukes or fleas or what not, to make an effort and adapt themselves, lead them now to their romantic and beneficial nuptials, while the Theory of Natural Selection grinds its teeth in the background and mutters "Foiled again."

But this third argument reinforces the first, in showing what is the matter with Mr. Belloc's ideas in this group of questions. He has got the whole business upside down. I rather blame the early Darwinians in this matter for using so inaccurate a phrase as the "Survival of the Fittest." It is to that phrase that most of Mr. Belloc's blunderings are due. Yet he ought not to have been misled. He had a summary of modern views before him. He criticises my *Outline of History,* he abuses it, and yet he has an extraordinary trick of getting out of its way whenever it swings near his brain-case. I warn the readers of that modest compendium expressly (and as early as page 16) that the juster phrase to use is not the Survival of the Fittest, but the Survival of the Fitter. I do what I can throughout to make them see this question not in terms of an individual, but in terms of the species.

Yet Mr. Belloc insists upon writing of "the Fittest" as a sort of conspicuously competitive prize boy, a favourable "sport," who has to meet his female equivalent and breed a new variety. That is all the world away from the manner in which a biologist thinks of the process of specific life. He sees a species as a vast multitude of individuals in which those without individual advantages tend to fail and those with them tend to be left to continue the race. The most important fact is the general relative failure of the disadvantaged. The fact next in order of importance is the general relative survival of the advantaged. The most important consequence is that the average of the species moves in the direction of advantageous differences, moving faster or slower according to its rate of reproduction and the urgency of its circumstances—that is to say, to the severity of its death-rate. Any one particular individual may have any sort of luck; that does not affect the general result.

I do not know what Mr. Belloc's mathematical attainments are, or indeed whether he has ever learnt to count beyond zero. There is no evidence on that matter to go upon in these papers. But one may suppose him able to understand what an average is, and he must face up to the fact that the characteristics of a species are determined by its average specimens. This dickering about with fancy stories of abnormal nuptials has nothing to do with the Theory of Natural Selection. We are dealing here with large processes and great numbers, secular changes and realities broadly viewed.

I must apologise for pressing these points home. But I think it is worth while to take this opportunity of clearing up a system of foggy misconceptions about the Theory itself that may not be confined altogether to Mr. Belloc.

MR. BELLOC COMES TO HIS EVIDENCE

And now let us come to Mr. Belloc's second triad of arguments—his arguments, as he calls them, "from Evidence." The sole witness on Evidence called is his own sturdy self. He calls himself into the box, and I will admit he gives his testimony in a bluff, straightforward manner —a good witness. He says very properly that the

theory of Natural Selection repudiates any absolute fixity of species. But we have to remember
that the rate of change in any species is dependent
upon the balance between that species and its conditions, and if this remains fairly stable the
species may remain for as long without remarkable developments, or indulge in variations not
conditioned by external necessities. The classical
Lingula of the geological text-books, a warm-
water shell-fish, has remained much the same
creature throughout the entire record, for hundreds of millions of years it may be. It was suited
to its submarine life, and hardly any variation
was possible that was not a disadvantage. It
swayed about within narrow limits.

This admission of a practical stability annoys
Mr. Belloc; it seems to be a mean trick on the
part of the Theory of Natural Selection. He
rather spoils his case by saying that "according
to Natural Selection" the swallow ought to go on
flying "faster and faster with the process of
time." Until it bursts into flames like a meteor
and vanishes from our world? And the *Lingula*
ought to become more and more quiescent until it
becomes a pebble? Yet plainly there is nothing in
the Theory of Natural Selection to make the swallow fly any faster than its needs require. Excess
of swiftness in a swallow may be as disadvantage-
ous as jumping to conclusions can be to a controversialist.

But here is a statement that is spirited and yet tolerably fair:—

> "If Natural Selection be true, then what we call a Pig is but a fleeting vision; all the past he has been becoming a Pig, and all the future he will spend evolving out of Pigdom, and Pig is but a moment's phase in the eternal flux."

This overlooks the melancholy possibility of an extinction of Pigs, but it may be accepted on the whole as true. And against this Mr. Belloc gives us his word, for that upon examination is what his "Evidence" amounts to—that Types are Fixed. He jerks in capitals here in a rather convincing way. It is restrained of him, considering how great a part typography plays in his rhetoric, that he has not put it up in block capitals or had the paper perforated with the words: Fixed Types.

> "We have the evidence of our senses that we are surrounded by fixed types."

For weeks and months it would seem Mr. Belloc has walked about Sussex accumulating first-hand material for these disputations, and all this time the Pigs have remained Pigs. When he prodded them they squealed. They remained pedestrian in spite of his investigatory pursuit. Not one did he find "scuttling away" with a fore-limb, "half-

leg, half-wing.'' He has the evidence of his
senses also, I may remind him, that the world is
flat. And yet when we take a longer view we find
the world is round, and Pigs are changing, and
Sus Scrofa is not the beast it was two thousand
years ago.

Mr. Belloc is conscious of historical training,
and I would suggest to him that it might be an
improving exercise to study the Pig throughout
history and to compare the Pigs of the past with
the Pigs of a contemporary agricultural show. He
might inform himself upon the bulk, longevity,
appetites, kindliness, and general disposition of
the Pig to-day. He might realise then that the
Pig to-day, viewed not as the conservative occu-
pant of a Sussex sty, but as a species, was something just a little different as a whole, but different, definably different, from the Pig of two thousand or five thousand years ago. He might retort that the Pig has been the victim of selective
breeding and is not therefore a good instance of
Natural Selection, but it was he who brought Pigs
into this discussion. Dogs again have been
greatly moulded by man in a relatively short time,
and, again, horses. Almost all species of animals
and plants that have come into contact with man
in the last few thousand years have been greatly
modified by his exertions, and we have no records
of any detailed observations of structure or habits
of creatures outside man's range of interest before the last three or four centuries. Even man

himself, though he changes with relative slowness
because of the slowness with which he comes to
sexual maturity, has changed very perceptibly in
the last five thousand years.

Mr. Belloc a Fixed Type

Mr. Belloc says he has not ("Argument from
Evidence"). He says it very emphatically
("Crushing Argument from Evidence"—to adopt
the phraseology of his cross-heads). Let me refer
him to a recent lecture by Sir Arthur Keith
(Royal Society of Medicine, Nov. 16, 1925) for a
first gleam of enlightenment. He will realise a
certain rashness in his statement. I will not fill
these pages with an attempt to cover all the
changes in the average man that have gone on in
the last two or three thousand years. For example, in the face and skull, types with an edge-
to-edge bite of the teeth are giving place to those
with an overlapping bite; the palate is under-
going contraction, the physiognomy changes.
And so on throughout all man's structure. No
doubt one can find plentiful instances to-day of
people almost exactly like the people of five thousand years ago in their general physique. But
that is not the point. The proportions and so
forth that were exceptional then are becoming
prevalent now; the proportions that were prevalent then, now become rare. The average type
is changing. Considering that man only gets

through about four generations in a century, it is a very impressive endorsement of the theory of Natural Selection that he has undergone these palpable modifications in the course of a brief score of centuries. Mr. Belloc's delusion that no such modification has occurred may be due to his presumption that any modification would have to show equally in each and every individual. I think it is. He seems quite capable of presuming that.

Triumphant Demand of Mr. Belloc

Mr. Belloc's next Argument from Evidence is a demand from the geologist for a continuous "series of changing forms passing one into the other." He does not want merely "intermediate forms," he says; he wants the whole series— grandfather, father, and son. He does not say whether he insists upon a pedigree with the bones and proper certificates of birth, but I suppose it comes to that. This argument, I am afraid, wins, hands down. Mr. Belloc may score the point. The reprehensible negligence displayed by the lower animals in the burial of their dead, or even the proper dating of their own remains, leaves the apologist for the Theory of Natural Selection helpless before this simple requisition. It is true that we now have, in the case of the camels, the horses, and the elephants, an extraordinary display of fossil types, exhibiting step by step the development and differentiation of species and genera. But this, I take it, rather concerns his Third than his Second Argument from Evidence.

A MAGNIFICENT GENERALISATION

The third argument is essentially a display of Mr. Belloc's inability to understand the nature of the record of the rocks. I will assume that he knows what "strata" are, but it is clear that he does not understand that any uniform stratum indicates the maintenance of uniform conditions while it was deposited and an absence of selective stresses, and that when it gives place to another different stratum, that signifies a change in conditions, not only in the conditions of the place where the stratum is found, but in the supply of material. An estuary sinks and gives place to marine sands, or fresh water brings down river gravels which cover over an accumulation of shingle. Now if he will think what would happen to-day under such circumstances, he will realise that the fauna and flora of the stratum first considered will drift away and that another fauna and flora will come in with the new conditions. Fresh things will come to feed and wade and drown in the waters, and old types will no longer frequent them. The fossil remains of one stratum are very rarely directly successive to those below it or directly ancestral to those above it. A succession of forms is much more difficult and elusive to follow up, therefore, than Mr. Belloc imagines. And then if he will consider what happens to the rabbits and rats and mice on his Sussex estate, and how they die and what happens to their bodies, he may begin to realise just what proportion of the remains of these creatures is ever likely to find its way to fossilisation. Perhaps years pass without the bones of a single rabbit from the whole of England finding their way to a resting-place where they may become fossil. Nevertheless the rabbit is a very common animal. And then if Mr. Belloc will think of palæontologists, millions of years after this time, working at the strata that we are forming to-day, working at a gravel or sand-pit here or a chance exposure there, and prevented from any general excavation, and if he will ask himself what proportion of the rare few rabbits actually fossilised are likely to come to light, I think he will begin to realise for the first time in his life the tremendous "gappiness" of the geological record and how very childish and absurd is his demand for an unbroken series of forms. The geological record is not like an array of hundreds of volumes containing a complete history of the past. It is much more like a few score crumpled pages from such an array, the rest of the volumes having either never been printed, or having been destroyed or being inaccessible.

In his Third Argument from Evidence Mr. Belloc obliges us with a summary of this record

of the rocks, about which he knows so little.   I
need scarcely note here that the only evidence
adduced is his own inspired conviction.   No
"European" palæontologist or biologist is brought
out of the Humbert safe and quoted.   Here was
a chance to puzzle me dreadfully with something
"in French," and it is scandalously thrown away.
Mr. Belloc tells us, just out of his head, that instead of there being that succession of forms in
the geological record the Theory of Natural Selection requires, there are "enormously long periods
of stable type" and "(presumably) rapid periods
of transition."   That "presumably" is splendid;
scientific caution and all the rest of it—rapid
periods when I suppose the Creative Spirit got
busy and types woke up and said, "Turn over;
let's change a bit."

There is really nothing to be said about this
magnificent generalisation except that it is pure
Bellocking.   Wherever there is a group of strata,
sufficiently thick and sufficiently alike to witness to
a long-sustained period of slight alterations in
conditions, there we find the successive species ap-
proximating.   This is not a statement à la Belloc.
In spite of the chances against such a thing occur-
ring, and in defiance of Mr. Belloc's assertion that
it does not occur, there are several series of
forms in time, giving a practically direct succession of species.   Mr. Belloc may read about it
and at the same time exercise this abnormal lin-
guistic gift which sits upon him so gracefully, his

knowledge of the French language, in Deperet's *Transformations du Monde Animal,* where all these questions are conveniently summarised. There he will get the results of Waagen with a succession of Ammonites and also of Neumayr with *Paludina,* and there also he will get information about the sequence of the species of *Mastodon* throughout the Tertiary age and read about the orderly progress of a pig group, the *Brachyodus* of the Eocene and Oligocene. There is a touch of irony in the fact that his own special protégé, the Pig, should thus turn upon him and rend his Third Argument from Evidence.

More recondite for Mr. Belloc is the work of Hilgendorf upon *Planorbis,* because it is in German; but the drift of it is visible in the Palæontology wing of the London Natural History Museum, Room VIII. A species of these gasteropods was, during the slow processes of secular change, caught in a big lake, fed by hot springs. It underwent progressive modification into a series of successive new species as conditions changed through the ages. Dr. Klähms' specimens show this beautifully. Rowe's account of the evolutionary series in the genus *Micraster* (*Q.J.M.S.,* 1899) is also accessible to Mr. Belloc, and he will find other matter to ponder in Goodrich's *Living Organisms,* 1924. The finest series of all, longer in range and completer in its links, is that of the Horse. There is an excellent little pamphlet by Matthew and Chubb, well illustrated, *The Evolu-*

tion of the Horse, published by the American Museum of Natural History, New York, so plain, so simple, so entirely and humiliatingly destructive of Mr. Belloc's nonsensical assertions, that I pray him to get it and read it for the good of his really very unkempt and neglected soul.

Thus we observe that Mr. Belloc does not know the facts in this case of Natural Selection, and that he argues very badly from such facts as he misconceives. It is for the reader to decide which at the end is more suitable as a laughing-stock—the Theory of Natural Selection or Mr. Belloc. And having thus studied this great Catholic apologist as an amateur biologist and arrived at the result, we will next go on to consider what he has to say about the origins of mankind—and Original Sin.

IV

MR. BELLOC'S ADVENTURES AMONG THE SUB-MEN: MANIFEST TERROR OF THE NEANDERTHALER

FROM Mr. Belloc's feats with Natural Selection we come to his adventures among his ancestors and the fall of man. These are, if possible, even more valiant than his beautiful exposure of the "half-educated assurance" of current biological knowledge. He rushes about the arena, darting from point to point, talking of my ignorance of the "main recent European work in Anthropology," and avoiding something with extraordinary skill and dexterity. What it is he is avoiding I will presently explain. No one who has read my previous articles need be told that not a single name, not a single paper, is cited from that galaxy of "main recent European" anthropology. With one small exception. There is a well-known savant, M. Marcellin Boule, who wrote of the Grottes de Grimaldi in 1906. Some facetious person seems to have written to Mr. Belloc and told him that M. Boule in 1906 "definitely proved the exact opposite" of the conclusions given by Mr. Wright in his *Quaternary Ice Age* (1914), and quoted in my *Outline*. Mr. Belloc

writes this down, elevates M. Boule to the mag-
nificence of "Boule" simply and follows up with
the habitual insults. By counting from his one
fixed mathematical point, *zero* in some dimension
unknown to me, he concludes that I must be twenty
years out of date, though the difference between
1906 and 1914, by ordinary ways of reckoning,
is really not minus twenty but plus eight.

The same ungracious humorist seems to have
stuffed up Mr. Belloc with a story that for the
last twenty years the climate of the earth has
ceased to vary with the eccentricity of the earth's
orbit, and that any natural consequences of the
procession of the equinoxes no longer occur; that
climate has, in fact, cut loose from astronomical
considerations, and that you can find out all about
it in the *Encyclopædia Britannica*. You cannot.
Mr. Belloc should have tried. Some day he must
find time to puzzle out M. Boule's curve of oscilla-
tion of the Mediterranean and correlate it with
Penck's, and go into the mystery of certain Moustierian implements that M. Boule says are not
Moustierian; and after that he had better read
over the little discussion about changes of climate
in the *Outline of History*—it is really quite simply
put—and see what it is I really said and what his
leg-pulling friend has been up to with him in that
matter. It may be kinder to Mr. Belloc to help
him with a hint. Croll made an excellent book
in which he pointed out a number of astronomical
processes which must produce changes of climate.

He suggested that these processes were sufficient to account for the fluctuations of the glacial age. They are not. But they remain perfectly valid causes of climatic variation. Croll is no more done for than Darwin is done for. That is where Mr. Belloc's friend let Mr. Belloc down.

But Mr. Belloc does not always work on the information of facetious friends, and sometimes one is clearly in the presence of the unassisted expert controversialist. When, for example, I say that the Tasmanians are not racially Neanderthalers, but that they are Neanderthaloid, he can bring himself to alter the former word also to Neanderthaloid in order to allege an inconsistency. And confident that most of his Catholic readers will not check him back by my book, he can ascribe to me views about race for which there is no shadow of justification. But it is disagreeable to me to follow up such issues, they concern Mr. Belloc much more than they do the living questions under discussion, and I will not even catalogue what other such instances of unashamed controversy occur.

Mr. Belloc as Iconoclast

In the course of the darting to and fro amongst human and sub-human pre-history, Mr. Belloc criticises me severely for quoting Sir Arthur Keith's opinion upon the Piltdown remains. I have followed English authorities. All these re-

mains are in England, and so they have been
studied at first hand mostly by English people.
No one can regret this insularity on the part of
Eoanthropus more than I do, but it leaves Mr.
Belloc's "European opinion on the whole" re-
jecting Sir Arthur Keith as a rather more than
usually absurd instance of Mr. Belloc's distinctive
method. *"What* European opinion?" you ask.
Mr. Belloc does not say. Probably Belloking of
Upsala and Bellokopoulos of Athens. Mr. Belloc
—forgetting that in an earlier edition of the *Outline* I give a full summary of the evidence in this
case, up-to-date—informs his Catholic audience
that I have apparently read nothing about the
Piltdown vestige but an "English work." And
then he proceeds to fall foul of the "restoration"
of *Eoanthropus*. It is an imaginary picture of
the creature, and I myself think that the artist
has erred on the human side. Mr. Belloc objects
to all such restorations.

Well, we have at least a saucerful of skull fragments and a doubtful jawbone to go upon, and
the picture does not pretend to be, and no reader
can possibly suppose it to be, anything but a
tentative restoration. But why a great Catholic
apologist of all people, the champion of a Church
which has plastered the world with portraits of
the Virgin Mary, of the Holy Family, and with
pictures of saints and miracles in the utmost pro-
fusion, without any warning to the simple-minded
that these gracious and moving figures to which

they give their hearts may be totally unlike the beings they profess to represent—why he should turn iconoclast and object to these modestly propounded restorations passes my comprehension. At Cava di Tirrene near Naples I have been privileged to see, in all reverence, a hair of the Virgin, small particles of St. Peter, and other evidences of Christianity; and they did not seem to me to be so considerable in amount as even the *Eoanthropus* fragments. And again, in this strange outbreak of iconoclastic rage, he says:—

"Again, we have the coloured picture of a dance of American Red Indians round a fire solemnly presented as a 'reconstruction' of Palæolithic society."

He has not even observed that the chief figures in that picture are copied directly from the actual rock paintings of Palæolithic men although this is plainly stated.

Mr. Belloc Discovers a Mare's-Nest

And yet he must have looked at the reproductions of these rock paintings given in the *Outline*. Because in his ninth paper he comes out with the most wonderful of all the mare's-nests he has discovered in the *Outline of History,* and it concerns these very pictures. You see there is an account of the Reindeer men who lived in France and

North Spain, and it is said of them that it is doubtful if they used the bow. Mr. Belloc declares that
it is my bitter hatred of religion that makes me
say this, but indeed it is not. It is still doubtful
if the Reindeer hunters had the bow. The fires
of Smithfield would not tempt me to say certainly
either that they had it or that they did not have
it, until I know. But they seem to have killed the
reindeer and the horse and bison by spearing
them. Mr. Belloc may have evidence unknown to
the rest of mankind in that Humbert safe of his,
otherwise that is the present state of our knowledge. But, as I explain on pages 56 and 57 in
language that a child might understand, simul-
taneously with that reindeer-hunting life in the
north there were more advanced (I know the word
will disgust Mr. Belloc with its horrid suggestion
of progress, but I have to use it) Palæolithic people scattered over the greater part of Spain and
reaching into the South of France who had the
bow. It says so in the text: "Men carry bows"
runs my text, describing certain rock pictures re-
produced in my book. I wrote it in the text; and
in the legends that are under these pictures,
legends read and approved by me, the statement
is repeated. The matter is as plain as daylight
and as plainly stated. Mr. Belloc will get if he
says over to himself slowly: "Reindeer men, bows
doubtful; Azilian, Capsian men to the south, bows
certainly." And now consider Mr. Belloc, weav-
ing his mare's-nest:—

"Upon page 55 he writes, concerning the Palæolithic man of the cave drawings, this sentence: *it is doubtful if they knew of the bow.*'

"When I first read that sentence, I was so staggered, I could hardly believe I had read it right."

"That a person pretending to teach popular prehistorical science in 1925 should tell us of the cave painters that it was *doubtful if they knew of the bow*' seemed to me quite out of nature.

"It was the more extraordinary because here before me, in Mr. Wells's own book, were reproductions of these cave paintings, with the bow and the arrow appearing all over them! Even if he did not take the trouble to look at the pictures that were to illustrate his book, and left that department (as he probably did) to hack work, he ought, as an ordinary educated man, to have known the ultimate facts of the case.

"Palæolithic man was an archer, and an archer with an efficient weapon.

"The thing is a commonplace; only gross ignorance can have overlooked it; but, as I have said, there is a cause behind that ignorance. Mr. Wells would not have made this enormous error if he had not been possessed with the necessity of making facts fit in with his theology."

THE CHASING OF MR. BELLOC BEGINS

There is a real splendour in these three almost consecutive passages. And note incidentally how this facile controversialist bespatters also my helpers and assistants. They do "hack work." Palæolithic man, speaking generally, was *not* an archer. Only the later Palæolithic men, dealing with a smaller quarry than the reindeer, seem to have used the bow. Manifestly it is not I who am fitting my facts with my theology here, but Mr. Belloc. He is inventing an error which is incredible even to himself as he invents it, and he is filling up space as hard as he can with indignation at my imaginary offence.

Why is he going on like this? In the interests of that Catholic soul in danger? Possibly. But his pen is running so fast here, it seems to me, not so much to get to something as to get away from something. The Catholic soul most in danger in these papers of Mr. Belloc's is Mr. Belloc's, and the thing he is running away from through these six long disputations is a grisly beast, neither ape nor true man, called the Neanderthaler, *Homo Neanderthalensis*. This *Homo Neanderthalensis* is the real "palæolithic" man. For three-quarters of the "palæolithic" age he was the only sort of man. The Reindeer men, the Capsian men, are "modern" beside him. He was no more an archer than he was an electrical engineer. He was no more an artist than Mr. Belloc is a man of science.

Instead of bothering with any more of the poor little bits of argey-bargey about this or that detail in my account of the earlier true men that

Mr. Belloc sees fit to make—instead of discussing whether these first human savages, who drew and painted like Bushmen and hunted like Labrador Indians, did or did not progress in the arts of life before they passed out of history, let me note now the far more important matters that he refuses to look at.

Mr. Belloc makes a vast pother about *Eoanthropus,* which is no more than a few bits of bone; he says nothing of the other creature to whom I have devoted a whole chapter: the man that was not a man. Loud headlines, challenging section headings, appeal in vain to Mr. Belloc's averted mind. Of this Neanderthal man we have plentiful evidence, and the collection increases every year. Always in sufficiently old deposits, and always with consistent characteristics. Here is a creature which not only made implements but fires, which gathered together ornamental stones, which buried its dead. Mr. Belloc says burying the dead is a proof of a belief in immortality. And this creature had strange teeth, differing widely from the human, more elaborate and less bestial; it had a differently hung head; it was chinless, it had a non-opposable thumb. Says M. Boule, the one anthropologist known to Mr. Belloc: "In its absence of forehead the Neanderthal type strikingly resembles the anthropoid apes." And he adds that it "must have possessed only a rudimentary psychic nature . . . markedly inferior to that of any modern race." When I heard that Mr. Belloc was going to explain and answer the *Outline of History*, my thought went at once to this creature. What would Mr. Belloc say of it? Would he put it before or after the Fall? Would he correct its anatomy by wonderful new science out of his safe? Would he treat it like a brother and say it held by the most exalted monotheism, or treat it as a monster made to mislead wicked men?

He says nothing! He just walks away whenever it comes near him.

But I am sure it does not leave him. In the night, if not by day, it must be asking him: "Have I a soul to save, Mr. Belloc? Is that Heidelberg jawbone one of us, Mr. Belloc, or not? You've forgotten me, Mr. Belloc. For four-fifths of the Palæolithic age I was 'man.' There was no other. I shamble and I cannot walk erect and look up at heaven as you do, Mr. Belloc, but dare you cast me to the dogs?"

No reply.

The poor Neanderthaler has to go to the dogs, I fear, by implication, for Mr. Belloc puts it with all the convincing force of italics, that *"Man is a fixed type."* We realise now why he wrote the four wonderful chapters about Natural Selection that we have done our best to appreciate. It was to seem to establish this idea of *fixed types*. Man had to be shown as a "Fixed Type" for reasons that will soon be apparent. Apart from Mr. Belloc's assertion, there is no evidence that man is any exception to the rest of living creatures. He changes. They all change. All this remarkable discourse about bows or no bows and about the high thinking and simple living of these wandering savages of twenty or more thousand years ago, which runs through half a dozen papers, seems to be an attempt to believe that these early men were creatures exactly like ourselves; and an attempt to believe that the more animal savages of the preceding hundred thousand years did not for all practical purposes exist at all. An attempt to believe and induce belief; not an attempt to demonstrate. Mr. Belloc emerges where he went in, with much said and nothing proved, and the *Outline* undamaged by his attack. And emerging he makes a confession that he never was really concerned with the facts of the case at all. "Sympathy or antagonism with the Catholic faith is the only thing of real importance in attempting to teach history"—and there you are! All these argumentative gesticulations, all these tortured attempts to confute, are acts of devotion to Mr. Belloc's peculiar vision of the Catholic faith.

I am afraid it is useless for me to suggest a pilgrimage to Mr. Belloc, or I would ask him to visit a popular resort not two hours by automobile from the little corner of France in which I am wont to shelter my suburban Protestantism from the too bracing English winter. That is the caves at Rochers Rouges, at which, as it happens, his one quoted authority, M. Boule, worked for

several years. There in an atmosphere entirely
"Latin" and "continental," under the guidance
of Signor Alfredo Lorenzi, he can see for himself his Fixed Type Man at successive levels of
change. No northern man need be with him when
he faces the facts of these caves; no Protestant
shadow need dog his steps; his French, that rare
distinguished gift, will be understood, and he may
even air such Provençal or Italian as he is master of. The horrid Neanderthaler is not in evidence. But there, protected by glass covers, he
will be able to see the skeletons of Cro-Magnon
man and Grimaldi man lying in the very positions
in which they were discovered. He will see for
himself the differences of level at which they were
found and have some help in imagining the ages
that separate the successive types. He will note
massiveness of skull and protrusion of jaw. He
will see the stone implements they used, the ashes
of their fires, and have some material for imagining the quality of their savagery. He can hunt
about for arrow-heads to bear out his valiant assertion that Palæolithic man was "an archer with
an efficient weapon." He will hunt until stoop-
ing and the sunshine make him giddy, in vain.
And then, with these bones fresh in his mind, he
should go to the Museum at Monaco and see the
skeleton of a modern human being. He will find
no end of loud talk and valiant singing and good
red wine necessary before he can get back to his
faith in man as a *Fixed Type*.

Where Was the Garden of Eden?

It is extremely difficult to find out what Mr.
Belloc, as a representative Catholic, believes
about human origins. I was extremely curious
to get the Catholic view of these matters, and I
heard of the advent of these articles with very
great pleasure, because I thought I should at last
be able to grasp what I had hitherto failed to understand in the Catholic position. But if Mr.
Belloc has said all that there is to say for Catholicism upon these points, Catholicism is bankrupt.
He assures me that to believe in the Biblical account of the Creation is a stupid Protestant tendency, and that Catholics do not do anything of
the sort. His attitude towards the Bible throughout is one almost of contempt. It is not for me
to decide between Christians upon this delicate
issue. And Catholics, I gather, have always believed in Evolution and are far above the intellectual level of the American Fundamentalist. It
is very important to Catholic self-respect to keep
that last point in mind. Catholic evolution is a
queer process into which "Design" makes occasional convulsive raids; between which raids species remain "fixed"; but still it is a sort of Evolution. My peasant neighbours in Provence, devout
Catholics and very charming people, have not the
slightest suspicion that they are Evolutionists,
though Mr. Belloc assures me they are.

But, in spite of this smart Evolutionary town wear of the Church, it has somehow to be believed by Catholics that "man" is and always has been and will be the same creature, "fixed." That much Mr. Belloc gives us reiteratively. A contemporary writer, the Rev. Morris Morris, has written an interesting book, *Man Created During Descent,* to show that man's immortal soul was injected into the universe at the beginning of the Neolithic period, which makes those Azilians and Capsians, with their bows and carvings, mere animals. The new Belloc-Catholic teaching is similar, but it puts the human beginnings earlier. Somewhen after the Chellean and Moustierian periods, and before the Reindeer men, I gather that "man" appeared, according to Catholic doctrines, exactly what he is now. Or rather better. He was clad in skins and feathers, smeared with paint, a cave-hunting wanderer with not even a dog at his heels; but he was, because Mr. Belloc says so, a devout monotheist and had a lucid belief in personal immortality. His art was pure and exalted—there were little bone figures of steatopygous women in evidence. He had no connection with the Neanderthal predecessor—or else he had jumped miraculously out of the Neanderthaler's bestial skin. Sometimes it seems to be one thing and sometimes the other. But all that stuff about Adam and Eve and the Garden and the Tree and the Serpent, so abundantly fig-

ured in Catholic painting and sculpture, seems to
have dropped out of this new version of Catholic
truth.

Yet those pictures are still shown to the faithful! And what the Fall becomes in these new
revelations of Catholicism, or whether there was
a Fall, historically speaking, Mr. Belloc leaves in
the densest obscurity. I have read and re-read
these articles of his, and I seek those lucid Latin
precisions he has promised me in vain. Was and
is that Eden story merely symbolical, and has
the Church always taught that it is merely symbolical? And if so, what in terms of current
knowledge do these symbols stand for? Is it
symbolical of some series of events in time or is
it not? If it is, when and what were the events
in time? And if it is not, but if it is symbolical
of some experience or adventure or change in the
life of each one of us, what is the nature of that
personal fall? What is the significance of the
Garden, the Innocence, the Tree, the Serpent?
To get anything clear and hard out of Mr. Belloc's papers in reply to these questions is like
searching for a diamond in a lake of skilly. I
am left with the uncomfortable feeling that Mr.
Belloc is as vague and unbelieving about this fundamental Catholic idea as the foggiest of foggy
Protestants and Modernists, but that he has
lacked the directness of mind to admit as much
even to himself. Yet surely the whole system of
salvation, the whole Christian scheme, rests upon

the presumption of a fall. Without a fall, what is the value of salvation? Why redeem what has never been lost? Without a condemnation what is the struggle? What indeed, in that case, is the Catholic Church about?

What modern thought is about is a thing easier to explain. In the *Outline of History,* against which Mr. Belloc is rather carping than levelling criticism, there is set out, as the main form of that *Outline,* a progressive development of conscious will in life. It is not a form thrust upon the massed facts by any fanatical prepossession; it is a form they insisted upon assuming under my summarising hand. What is going on in this dispute is not that I am beating and putting over my ideas upon Mr. Belloc or that he is beating and putting over his ideas upon me, but that the immense increase of light and knowledge during the past century is imposing a new realisation of the quality and depth and import of life upon us both, and that I am acquiescent and he is recalcitrant. I judge his faith by the new history, and he judges the new history by his faith.

V

FIXITY OR PROGRESS

I AM glad to say that we are emerging now from the worst of the controversial stuff, irritating and offensive, in which Mr. Belloc is so manifestly my master, and coming to matters of a more honest interest.

I have stuck to my argument through the cut and slash, sneer and innuendo of Mr. Belloc's first twelve papers. I have done my best to be kind and generous with him. I have made the best excuses I can for him. I have shown how his oddities of bearing and style arise out of the difficulties of his position, and how his absurd reasonings about Natural Selection and his deliberate and tedious bemuddlement of the early Palæolithic sub-men with the late Reindeer men and the Capsian men are all conditioned by the necessity he is under to declare and believe that "man" is, as he puts it, a "Fixed Type," the same in the past and now and always. He is under this necessity because he believes that otherwise the Christian faith cannot be made to stand up as a rational system, and because, as I have shown by a quotation of his own words, he makes their com-

patibility with his idea of Catholic teaching his
criterion in the acceptance or rejection of facts.

I will confess I do not think that things are as
bad as this with Christianity. I believe a far better case could be made for Catholicism by an in-
sistence that its value and justification lie in the
change and in the direction of the human will, in
giving comfort and consolation and peace, in pro-
ducing saints and beautiful living; and that the
truth of the history it tells of space and time is
entirely in relation to the development of these
spiritual aspects, and has no necessary connection whatever with scientific truth. This line of
thought is no novelty, and I do not see why Catholics should not keep to it and leave the outline of
history alone. I do not say that it is a line of
apologetics that would convince me altogether,
but it is one that would need far more arduous
discussion and merit, far more respect than Mr.
Belloc's *a priori* exploits, his limping lizards and
flying pigs.

But it is not my business to remind Catholics
of their own neglected philosophers, and clearly
the publication of Mr. Belloc's articles by the
Universe, the *Catholic Bulletin,* and the *Southern
Cross* shows that the Catholic world of to-day is
stoutly resolved to treat the fall of man and his
unalterable nature as matters of fact, even if they
are rather cloudy matters of fact, and to fight the
realities of modern biology and anthropology to
the last ditch.

So the Catholics are pinned to this dogma of the fixity of man and thereby to a denial of progress. This vale of tears, they maintain, is as a whole a stagnant lake of tears, and there is no meaning to it beyond the spiritual adventures of its individual lives. Go back in time or forward, so long as man has been or will be, it is all the same. You will find a world generally damned, with a select few, like Mr. Belloc, on their way to eternal beatitude. That is all there is to the spectacle. There is, in fact, no outline of history; there is just a flow of individual lives; there is only birth and salvation or birth and damnation. That, I extract from Mr. Belloc and other contemporary writers, is the Catholic's vision of life.

THE IDEA OF FIXED HUMANITY

And it is not only the Catholic vision of life. It is a vision far more widely accepted. I would say that, if we leave out the ideas of damning or beatitude, it is the "common-sense" vision of the world. The individual life is, to common-sense, all that matters, the entire drama. There is from this popular and natural point of view no large, comprehensive drama in which the individual life is a subordinate part. Just as to the untutored mind the world is flat, just as to Mr. Belloc during his biological research work in Sussex the species of pig remained a "fixed type," so to the common intelligence life is nothing more

or less than "Me," an unquestioned and unana-
lysed Me, against the universe.

The universe may indeed be imagined as ruled
over and pervaded by God, and this world may
be supposed to have extensions of hell and
heaven; all sorts of pre-natal dooms and debts
may affect the career of the Me, but nevertheless
the Me remains in the popular mind, nobbily integral, one and indivisible, and either it ends and
the drama ends with it, or it makes its distinct
and special way to the Pit, or, with Belloc and
the Catholic community, to the beatitude he an-
ticipates.

The individual self is primary to this natural,
primitive, and prevalent mode of thinking. But
it is not the only way of thinking about life. The
gist of the *Outline of History* is to contradict this
self-centred conception of life and show that this
absolute individualism of our thought and des-
tinies is largely illusory. We do not live in ourselves, as we so readily imagine we do; we are
contributory parts in the progress of a greater
being which is life, and which becomes now conscious of itself through human thought.

The Fundamental Issue

Now here I think we get down, beneath all the
frothings and bespatterings of controversy, to the
fundamental difference between Mr. Belloc and
myself. It is this which gives our present con-

troversy whatever claim it can have to attention. Neither Mr. Belloc nor myself is a very profound or exhaustive philosopher. In ourselves we are very unimportant indeed. But we have this in common, that we can claim to be very honestly expressive of the mental attitudes of clearly defined types of mind, and that we are sharply antithetical types.

By nature and training and circumstances Mr. Belloc stands for the stout sensible fellow who believes what he sees; who considers that his sort always has been and always will be; who stands by accepted morals and time-honoured ways of eating and drinking and amusement; who loves—and grips as much as he can of—the good earth that gives us food for our toil; who begets children honestly by one beloved wife until she dies and then repeats the same wholesome process with the next; who believes in immortality lest he should be sorry to grow old and die; who trusts in the Church and its teaching because visibly the Church is a great and impressive fact, close at hand and extremely reassuring; who is a nationalist against all strangers because, confound it! there are nations, and for Christendom against all pagans; who finds even Chinamen and Indians remote and queer and funny. I do not think that is an unfair picture of the ideals of Mr. Belloc and of his close friend and ally, Mr. Chesterton, as they have spread them out for us; and I admit they are warm and rosy ideals. But they are ideals and not realities. The real human being upon this swift-spinning planet is not that stalwart, entirely limited, fixed type resolved to keep so, stamping about the flat world under God's benevolent sky, eating, drinking, disputing, and singing lustily, until he passes on to an eternal individual beatitude with God and all the other blessed ones. He is less like that every day, and more and more conscious of the discrepancy.

I have read and admired and sympathised with the work of Mr. Belloc and Mr. Chesterton since its very beginnings, but I find throughout it all a curious defensive note. It may be I attribute distresses to them that they do not feel. But it seems to me they are never quite sure in their minds about this "fixed" human being of theirs— the same yesterday, now, and for ever. Mr. Belloc must be puzzled not a little by that vast parade of Evolution through the immeasurable ages which he admits has occurred—a parade made by the Creative Force for no conceivable reason, since a "fixed type" might just as well have been created straight away. He must realise that if man is the beginning and end of life, then his Creator has worked within fantastically disproportionate margins both of space and time. And in his chapters upon animal and human origins Mr. Belloc's almost obstinate ignorance of biological facts, his fantastic "logic," his pathetic and indubitably honest belief in his non-existent "European authorities," his fumbling and evasion about Palæolithic man, and above all his petty slights and provocations to those whose views jar upon him, have nothing of the serenity of a man assured of his convictions, and all the irritability and snatching at any straw of advantage of a man terribly alarmed for his dearest convictions. When Mr. Belloc gets to his beatitude he will feel like a fish out of water. I believe Mr. Belloc and his friend Mr. Chesterton are far too intelligent not to be subconsciously alive to the immense and increasing difficulties of their positions, and that they are fighting most desperately against any conscious realisation of the true state of affairs.

The Idea of Progressive Humanity

It happens that my circumstances, and perhaps my mental temperament, have brought my mind into almost dramatic opposition to that of Mr. Belloc. While his training was mainly in written history, the core of mine was the analytical exercises of comparative anatomy and palæontology. I was brought up upon the spectacle of life in the universe as a steadily changing system. My education was a modern one, upon material and questionings impossible a hundred years ago. Things that are fundamental and commonplaces to me have come, therefore, as belated, hostile, and extremely distressing challenges to the satisfactions and acceptances of Mr. Belloc.

Now, this picture of a fixed and unprogressive humanity working out an enormous multitude of individual lives from birth to either eternal beatitude or to something not beatitude, hell or destruction or whatever else it may be that Mr. Belloc fails to make clear is the alternative to beatitude—this picture, which seems to be necessary to the Catholic and probably to every form of Christian faith, and which is certainly necessary to the comfort of Mr. Belloc, has no validity whatever for my mind. It is no more possible in my thought as a picture of reality than that ancient cosmogony which made the round earth rest upon an elephant, which stood upon a tortoise, which stood upon God-knows-what.

I do not know how the universe originated, or what it is fundamentally; I do not know how material substance is related to consciousness and will; I doubt if any creature of my calibre is capable of knowing such things; but at least I know enough to judge the elephant story and the fixed humanity story absurd. I do not know any convincing proof that Progress *must* go on; I find no invincible imperative to progressive change in my universe; but I remark that progressive change does go on, and that it is the form into which life falls more and more manifestly as our analysis penetrates and our knowledge increases. I set about collecting what is known of life and the world in time and space, and I find the broad outline falls steadily and persistently into a story of life appearing and increasing in range, power, and co-operative unity of activity. I see knowledge increasing and human power increasing, I see ever-increasing possibilities before life, and I see no limits set to it all. Existence impresses me as a perpetual dawn. Our lives, as I apprehend them, swim in expectation. This is not an outline I have thrust upon the facts; it is the outline that came naturally as the facts were put in order.

And it seems to me that we are waking up to the realisation that the individual life does not stand alone, as people in the past have seemed to imagine it did, but that it is far truer to regard it as an episode in a greater life, which progresses and which need not die. The episode begins and ends, but life goes on.

Mr. Belloc is so far removed from me mentally that he is unable to believe that this, clearly and honestly, is how I see things; he is moved to explain it away by saying that I am trying to "get rid of a God," that I am a rotten Protestant, that this is what comes of being born near London, that if I knew French and respected the Gentry all this would be different, and so on, as the attentive student of his great apology for Catholicism has been able to observe. But all the while he is uncomfortably on the verge of being aware that I am a mere reporter of a vast mass of gathered knowledge and lengthened perspectives that towers up behind and above his neat and jolly

marionette show of the unchanging man and his
sins and repentances and mercies, his astonishing
punishments, and his preposterous eternal reward
among the small eternities of the mediæval imagination. I strut to no such personal beatitude. I
have no such eternity of individuation. The life
to which I belong uses me and will pass on beyond me, and I am content.

The New Thought and the Old

Mr. Belloc is completely justified in devoting
much more than half his commentary to these fundamental issues and dealing with my account of
the appearance of Christianity and the story of
the Church much more compactly. It is this difference at the very roots of our minds which matters to us, and it is the vital question we have
to put before the world. The rest is detail. I
do believe and assert that a new attitude to life,
a new and different vision of the world, a new
moral atmosphere and a different spirit of con-
duct, is coming into human affairs, as a result
of the scientific analysis of the past hundred
years. It is only now reaching such a clearness
of definition that it can be recognised for what
it is and pointed out.

The essential distinction of the newer thought
in the world is in its denial of the permanence
of the self and in its realisation of the self's comparative unimportance. Even in our individual

lives we are increasingly interested in common
and generalised things. The older commoner life,
the religious life just as much as the most worldly
life, seems to us excessively self-conscious. The
religious life, its perpetual self-examination for
sin and sinful motives, its straining search after
personal perfection, appears in the new light
as being scarcely less egotistical than a dandy's.
And this new way of living and thinking is
directly linked on to the idea of progress,
which makes life in general far more interesting
than any individual life can be, just as the self-
centred life, whether it be religious and austere
or vain or self-indulgent, is directly connected
with the old delusions of permanence which rob
life in general of any sustained interest. When
one is really persuaded that there is nothing new
under the sun, then there is nothing worth living
for whatever outside the personal adventure, the
dance between permanent individual beatitude or
permanent individual damnation.

As this modern conception of life as a process
of progressive change in which individuality of
our order can be sometimes excessively exag-
gerated as it has been in the past and sometimes
minimised as is happening now—as this conception establishes itself, it changes the spirit of living and the values of our general ideas about living profoundly. Lit only by a very bright light
held low, an ordinary road becomes a tangle of
vivid surfaces and black shadows, and you cannot

tell a puddle or a gutter from a ditch or a preci-
pice. But in diffused daylight you can see the
proportions of every irregularity. So too with
changing illumination our world alters its aspects,
and things that once seemed monstrous and final
are seen to be mere undulations in a practicable
progress. We can realise now, as no one in the
past was ever able to realise it, that man is a
creature changing very rapidly from the life of
a rare and solitary great ape to the life of a social and economic animal. He has traversed most
of this tremendous change of phase in something
in the nature of a million years. His whole being,
mind and body alike, betrays the transition. We
can trace the mitigations of his egotism through
the development of religious and customary re-
straints. The recent work of the psycho-analyst
enables us to understand something of the intricate system of suppressions and inhibitions
that this adaptation to a more and more complex
social life has involved. We begin to realise how
man has symbolised and personified his difficulties, and to comprehend the mechanisms of his
uncongenial but necessary self-restraint.

Old Wine in New Bottles

The disposition of those who apprehend this
outline of history that modern science has made
plain to us, and who see all life as a system of
progressive change, is by no means antagonistic

to religion. They realise the immense importance and the profound necessity of religion in this last great chapter of the story, the evolution of human society. But they see religion within the frame of fact; they do not, like Mr. Belloc, look through religion at fact. Man has accommodated his originally fierce and narrow egotism to the needs of an ever wider and more co-operative social life, very largely through the complex self-subjugations that religion has made possible. Within the shell and cover of religion the new less self-centred habits of mind have been able to develop. An immense mass of imaginative work, of mythology, of theology, that now seems tortuous, mystical, and fantastic, was necessary for the casting of the new moral being of socialised man. We seem to be entering upon a phase in which moral and intellectual education may be able to free themselves from the last vestiges of the mythology in which that new moral being was moulded; but it is ungracious and false to the true outline of history to deny the necessary part that the priest, the sacrifice, the magic ceremonial for tribal welfare, the early tribal religions, have played in this transfiguration of the sub-human into the modern human mind, upon which all our community rests to-day.

It is because of our sense of this continuity of our present dispositions with the religions upon which they are founded that so many of us are loth to part with all the forms and phrases of

the old creeds and all the disciplines of time-
honoured cults. Perhaps some of us (the present
writer in the crowd among others) have been over-
eager to read new significances into established
phrases, and clothe new ideas in the languages of
the old scheme of salvation. It may be we have
been pouring new wine into old bottles. It may
be better to admit frankly that if man is not fixed
Christianity is, and that mankind is now growing out of Christianity; that indeed mankind is
growing out of the idea of Deity. This does not
mean an end to religion, but it means a fresh
orientation of the religious life. It means a final
severance with those anthropomorphic concep-
tions of destiny, that interpretation of all things
in terms of personality and will with which religion began. For many of us that still means a
wrench and an effort. But the emphatic assertions of Mr. Belloc, the stand that Catholicism,
as he expounds it, makes against any progressive
adaptation to the new spirit in human life, may
render that effort easier.

In this examination of Mr. Belloc's opening and more fundamental attacks upon the *Outline of History* I have shown sufficiently that Mr. Belloc is incapable of evidence or discussion, that he imagines his authorities, that he is careless and ignorant as to his facts and slovenly and tricky in his logic. I have dealt kindly but adequately with his atrocious bad manners and his insolence and impudence. I do not think it is worth while to go on through the second half of his outpourings with any particularity. It is exactly the same kind of thing, but upon more familiar ground and less fundamental issues. Mr. Belloc quibbles. He falsifies. For example, he imagines traditions to reinforce the Gospel account of Christ's teaching and to show that the founder of Christianity was aware of his godhead and taught the doctrine of the Trinity; he declares—just out of his head—that I do not know it was the bull and not Mithra who was sacrificed in the system of Mithraism, though I state that quite plainly in a passage he has ventured to ignore. And so on. The wonderful methods of the Palæolithic bow story repeat themselves with variations, time after time. Why should I trouble to repeat the exposure in every case? I have done enough to demonstrate the quality of this effort to bluff and

94

bawl away accepted knowledge and manifest fact, and that is all that I set out to do.

And this apparently is the present state of Catholic teaching. This stuff I have examined is ance of organised Christianity, so far as there is representative stuff. This is the current utterance of organised Christianity, so far as there is any utterance, upon the doctrines of the Creation and the Fall—doctrines upon which rest the whole scheme of Christian salvation and the entire fabric of a Christian's faith.